E. East

TRINITY
COLLEGE LONDON PRESS

Take Your Bow

20 concert pieces for beginner string players

Violin & Piano

by Celia Cobb & Naomi Yandell

Published by
Trinity College London Press Ltd
trinitycollege.com

Registered in England
Company no. 09726123

Copyright © 2018 Trinity College London Press Ltd
First impression, February 2018

Cover design and illustrations by Ruth Keating for rkrk.co.uk

Printed in England by Caligraving Ltd

Contents

Take Your Bow is a collection of 20 concert pieces for beginner string players written by Celia Cobb and Naomi Yandell. Years of string teaching have given them the inspiration to produce pieces which will both delight and engage. Their imaginative writing strengthens rhythmic and stylistic concepts, whilst employing a variety of adventurous playing techniques that students will find to be a fun and achievable challenge.

Each piece is compatible with any of the other instruments in the series, in any combination, making it an excellent resource for individual or group teaching. *Take Your Bow* is available in 4 individual editions − for violin, viola, cello and double bass, each with piano accompaniment − and as a separate full score.

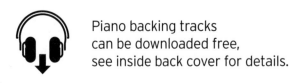

Piano backing tracks can be downloaded free, see inside back cover for details.

1. Off We Go

2. Marching to the Castle

3. Hornpipe

4. Too Much Sugar (Too Many Treats)

5. Brain Teaser Waltz

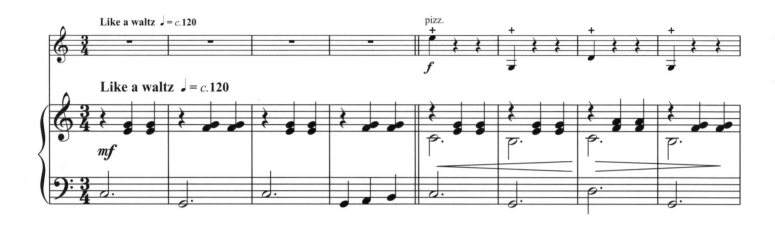

8

6. I Can Count to Five

7. Knock at the Door

8. Dancing the Tango

9. First in the Queue

10. Clockwork Clown

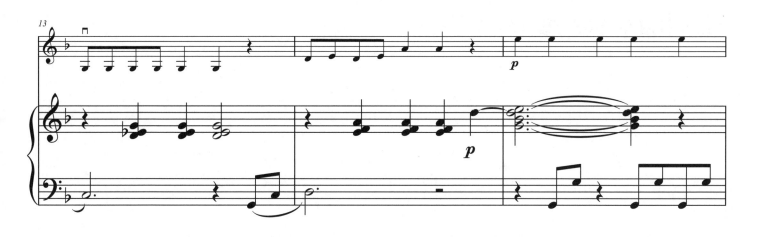

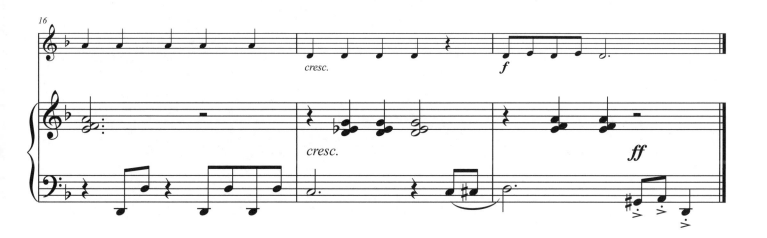

11. Hazy Days

12. How I Wonder What You Are

13. I'm So Happy

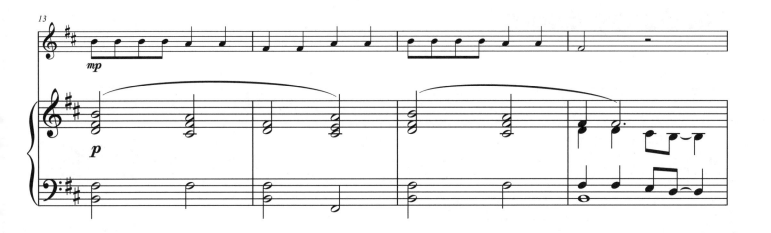

D.S. al Fine

D.S. al Fine

14. Bossy Boots

15. Sad Smile

16. On the Ranch

17. Busy Bee

18. Poem

19. Look at the Starlight

20. Birthday Bash

Piano Accompaniment Download Listing

For solo, or groups using violin, viola or cello:

Track no.

1 Off We Go

2 Marching to the Castle

3 Hornpipe

4 Too Much Sugar (Too Many Treats)

5 Brain Teaser Waltz

6 I Can Count to Five

7 Knock at the Door

8 Dancing the Tango

9 First in the Queue

10 Clockwork Clown

11 Hazy Days

12 How I Wonder What You Are

13 I'm So Happy

14 Bossy Boots

15 Sad Smile

16 On the Ranch

17 Busy Bee

18 Poem

19 Look at the Starlight

20 Birthday Bash

For solo, or groups using double bass:

Track no.

21 Off We Go

22 Marching to the Castle

23 Hornpipe

24 Too Much Sugar (Too Many Treats)

25 Brain Teaser Waltz

26 I Can Count to Five

27 Knock at the Door

28 Dancing the Tango

29 First in the Queue

30 Clockwork Clown

31 Hazy Days

32 How I Wonder What You Are

33 I'm So Happy

34 Bossy Boots

35 Sad Smile

36 On the Ranch

37 Busy Bee

38 Poem

39 Look at the Starlight

40 Birthday Bash

Piano accompaniments performed by Jeff Leach

 Piano backing tracks
can be downloaded free,
see inside back cover for details.